▲

on the cover

CONTEMPLATING IMMORTALITY

Watercolor by a Person Diagnosed with Cancer
New Hampshire, United States

It struck me how one minute, immortality seemed steadfast, but in the next, how vulnerable and uncertain my circle of life had become. After my initial introduction to breast cancer, I shifted gears and began to rely on my inner strength to move through this shadow of darkness to address my life-altering transformation with grace and fortitude. I did not think of cancer as a permanent setback or a death sentence. Losing my hair was not something I saw as shameful or unattractive. Cancer was a transformation that I accepted and moved on from.

Although cancer is still a speed bump in my journey through life, I am forever grateful for the bright sunny days that continue to surround me. Immortality seems steadfast once again!

THE ART OF LIVING WITH BREAST CANCER

When cancer affected the lives of these people and their families, it set off a spark that turned into a blaze of courage and determination. That blaze reveals itself in each of the pieces that make up this collection. They include works of hope, inspiration, and defiance that illuminate every facet of the experience.

DAWN OF A NEW DAY
see artwork narrative on page 7

◀ DAWN OF A NEW DAY
Oil by a Person Diagnosed with Cancer
New York, United States

I have breast cancer! You will notice that I said I have breast cancer, it does **not** have me! Cancer has not taken anything from me; I feel it has given me my life back! Cancer may be strong, but I am stronger! I am persistent and have a positive attitude! Even if I died, I'd cause such a ruckus up in heaven they'd send me right back! **I** choose, **not** cancer, and **I** choose to live! That is what my painting depicts! Dawn of a new day! A beautiful sunrise coming over the mountains persistent in their own right! The water, life sustaining, flowing freely down below, with new life in the foliage all around. Everything alive with such splendor and beauty, determined and bountiful, just like me!

left page
◀ PEARLS OF WISDOM
Mixed Media by a Person Diagnosed with Cancer
North Carolina, United States

My battle against breast cancer began with a special gift from my twin sister. Her gift was a card of encouragement and a pair of pearl earrings. The card featured an oyster and told the story of how it would fight a foreign object that had entered its shell. The oyster places layers upon layers of nacre to rid itself of the irritant. The oyster's battle ends with the creation of a precious pearl. The fight ahead of me would be much like the oyster's. Determined and wearing my earrings, I began my journey. My layers would be 17 chemo rounds and 33 radiation treatments. After my long and sometimes difficult journey, I too had created something beautiful. I am a strong woman who has survived breast cancer. Life is good now and maybe even a little better. Cancer has shown me what is important in my life and what I needed to let go. I celebrate the survivors and hope that all cancer patients still fighting will find their pearl.

◀ GO, CELLS, GO!
Mixed Media by a Family Member, Friend, or Caregiver
Iowa, United States

Two weeks after her sister's death from lung cancer, my grandma, Donna, was diagnosed with Stage 3A invasive ductal carcinoma breast cancer. She focused on the positive instead of the negative battles of double mastectomies, radiation, and chemotherapy effects—the tiny, healthy cells in her body battling big cancer cells. My hope with this art is that viewers fighting cancer may begin to focus their minds to join their cells' fight: to center their attention and energy on encouraging their bodies' most basic unit of life in its own fight against cancer. Start with the smallest and most important one first: healthy cells living and cancer cells dying; encourage good cells to fight this villain! Envision healthy cells living and fighting. Go, cells, go!

▲

PINK SPIKE

Photography by a Person Diagnosed with Cancer
Maryland, United States

Nineteen years ago, I discovered my breast lump. I had a mammogram, a sonogram, a biopsy, and surgery for stage II breast cancer. After six months of chemotherapy, I had breast reconstruction.

Before cancer, I was an artist printmaker, but during treatment and afterwards, I experimented with less physical forms of art.

While on vacation in the southwest, I photographed a series of my own shadow (with no hair visible), positioned to use unusual cacti as wigs.

This "Pink Spike" shadow portrait makes me laugh. During treatment, I was bald as an egg. Now that my hair has grown back, I am just thankful to have hair and I never have a bad hair day.

▲

RAIN WALK
Photography by a Person Diagnosed with Cancer
Massachusetts, United States

Walking through the rain can be an awakening of the spirit—one needs to be observant with all the senses open to discovery. This parallels my 25-year journey with breast cancer.

This journey has been a unique learning experience. The road has been both stormy and sunny and everything in between.

I have learned much during my journey. The appreciation of "what is" and the hope of "what can be" have been important aspects in my life. The changing seasons, the beauty that lives within each season, a smile from a friend or passing stranger, and the appreciation of those that journey with me are such positive influences.

I travel forward with the help of family, friends and caregivers.

Life is good in sun and rain.

NOT ALL IS BLACK AND WHITE
Mixed Media by a Person Diagnosed with Cancer
Kansas, United States

It could be anyone...it could be you…it could be me. This time, spring 2009, it was me. No explanation…no warning...no rhyme...no reason… only the diagnosis…breast cancer…what ???...me???...Time stops… not for the crepe myrtle…their growth bursts forth…as my cancer… engaging my thoughts and entangling me into their branches...moving me along through my journey…I see myself in the mirrors…interwoven throughout the roots and branches…lost…the cancer is growing… spreading throughout my body…alright then…surgery and treatment… later a calmness…and much later…color…brightness…joy…new hope...cheer…laughter…beauty…new beginnings…life…embracing each day…celebrating three years in remission.

WINNING
Pastel by a Person Diagnosed with Cancer
Ohio, United States

I feel as if I'm in a strange beauty pageant where cancer robs you of your femininity!

For my family breast cancer is most prevalent, as I've had two cousins develop it before my journey began. In 1992, at age 38, a lump in my left breast required a lumpectomy. The next year I had a total mastectomy, radiation and chemo. Four years later, my oldest sister underwent a lumpectomy, chemo, radiation, and a five-year drug treatment. Then, in 2007, my youngest sister was diagnosed. She was a OBRCA 2 carrier and died in 2010, so I had the test. Now I've had my right breast removed and next a hysterectomy. I have to stay healthy to watch my daughter's health. So for now, I'm winning!

THE ART OF VIEWING ART

THINK

Interpret what you see and give it
meaning. What is the story? What is
the mood? What is the artist trying
to communicate?

FOUR SEASONS
see artwork narrative on page 13

◄ FOUR SEASONS
Mixed Media by a Person Diagnosed with Cancer
Washington DC, United States

I've been through four seasons with cancer. My artwork is composed of several layers. It starts with a breast cancer ultrasound at the bottom, followed by a few rough and rustic layers—a cancer diagnosis in early 2013, a mastectomy, and more—until a very thin/delicate but healthy layer forms on the top.

New, fresh life makes its way through to the surface from my center of gravity and expands all around, enlightening the whole.

New life starts to bloom, and soon the warmth and brightness of summer completes this colorful and full-of-energy picture.

The fall leaves and winter colors have been covered almost completely. Their presence is and will remain somehow noticeable. They are fundamental pillars of who I am today.

---

left page
◄ FREE FALL
Acrylic by a Family Member, Friend, or Caregiver
North Carolina, United States

When my wife was diagnosed with breast cancer, there was an enormous amount of sorrow, apprehension and uncertainty. Our world had turned into a free fall. We had no control whatsoever. It was very difficult knowing that she was hurting and not being able to help make things better. Everything got turned around and the future was uncertain. We did not know where we would land.

We were in a free fall that we could not control. We tried to be strong for each other, but some days were very gray and cloudy. We fought the battle together and now my wife is a 2½-year survivor. Being on the other side, we celebrate life and are very happy for our future. I'm grateful today and enjoy our blessings. It's important to have gratitude and bask in the goodness of life.

◄ COURAGE CARRIES HOPE
Mixed Media by a Person Diagnosed with Cancer
Arizona, United States

A red-tailed hawk perched in our tree appears to have strength, courage and patience—necessary attributes to sustain me on my journey facing breast cancer. The hummingbird represents me. Once I was very active and independent, and now I rely more on others. The inner weavings on the hawk's feathers represent the medicines, professionals, family, and friends binding together to help me. I appreciate their love, care and support. The hawk is carrying me to sunshine. The circles of white within the sun hold outlines of butterflies representing dear friends whose souls have passed while I survive my journey. Dots in the clouds represent cancer research, still going in circles. The dots in the dark sky are souls who have passed on from cancer.

▲

TRUST FALL

Photography by a Person Diagnosed with Cancer
Texas, United States

trust fall [truhst] [fawl] noun: a trust-building activity often conducted as a group exercise in which a person deliberately allows herself to fall, relying on the other members of the group to catch her.

Having cancer felt like one big trust fall. My medical team tells me their recommendations for treating the tumor in my breast. They say, "Lean on." I hesitate in fear. Finally, I arrive at the moment when I put my trust in their advice and lean back while saying, "Falling!" "Fall on!" they reply. I let go of fear, hoping it will be worth it. I remind myself that trials bring strength and understanding that help us catch others. I surrender and find peace.

▲

CERTAINS LAPAIX AVEC REMISE, J'ESPERE QUE POUR URE CURE

Watercolor by a Person Diagnosed with Cancer
New Jersey, United States

Often, in foreign languages, words can sound so much more pleasant than they really are. However, in any language, cancer is the ugliest word. The title of my art translates (from French) roughly to, "Some peace with remission, I hope for a cure."

February, 2012, marked five years of being in remission after my second bout with triple negative breast cancer. I am only required to see an oncologist twice per year at this point, as well as my breast surgeon.

There is so much more peace in my life with remission, and I would certainly say this is a sweet thing.

The only thing I would find sweeter would be zero worries about recurrence, which would require a definitive end to cancer from a cure.

▲

LIFE'S THERAPY SESSIONS
Mixed Media by a Person Diagnosed with Cancer
Connecticut, United States

Can the goals of a 32-year-old, with breast cancer be obtained?

My son was 4 when I received the devastating diagnosis. All I could think of was getting him through kindergarten and in school all day.

Next goal, do I dare think about high school and college graduations—I was there.

A wedding—I had the best time, just because I was there.

Grandchildren? Maybe I prayed too hard, but beautiful twins were born, and I was there.

My next goal—will they remember me? I will teach them how to paint gourds, sew, quilt, and appreciate nature.

Well, they started kindergarten in September.

I turned 65 in February.

33 years and four bouts with cancer, life's therapy sessions.

▲

JUST A BIT OF GRAY...
Photography by a Person Diagnosed with Cancer
Arizona, United States

So often when we are given the news that cancer lives within our bodies, we only see the blackness of death. For the past 10 years, I have been chasing breast cancer and I have learned so much about the gray areas of my life.

Not just gray, but many times, brilliant colors of laughter, joy, love, friendships, and all those special moments I never took the time to truly experience before cancer. The day I accepted that I was going to die one day, because we all have that destiny to fulfill, was the day I truly began to live. Don't miss a moment… Shalom.

▲

JOURNEY TO VICTORY
Acrylic by a Family Member, Friend, or Caregiver
Texas, United States

Susan, my bride of 45 years, has successfully battled breast cancer twice over the last 21 years. My journey began, each time, when the word "cancer" was uttered.

Suddenly, your footing and balance is diminished. You begin to spiral downward. Out of control, your mind races. Events and possibilities have you swirling about. You feel disconnected and fall into moments of despair, trying not to bring down the spirits of the woman you love. You feel like you are falling headfirst into the dark pit of the unknown.

And then, one day, there comes a sense of new beginning. Out of the pit rises the butterfly of new hope. Each day is brighter until the cancer is gone. The journey to victory is complete.

ANGEL AND I
Oil by a Person Diagnosed with Cancer
Michigan, United States

The words "you have breast cancer" brought dark clouds of fear and doom. Using the reins of family, friends, surgeons, and support groups, Angel and I took a stormy ride through rough waters. My horse, Angel, took me to a calmer and brighter place. On the shore, I dismounted and felt safe at last and full of hope. I have love and gratitude for all who helped Angel and I ride through trying times— SET FREE.

SHE HAS THE GIFT
Pastel by a Family Member, Friend, or Caregiver
Washington, United States

I am the daughter of a four-time breast cancer survivor. She had radical mastectomies in 1968 and 1974, reoccurring tumors in 1995 and 2009. Through it all, she never once asked, "Why me?" Her attitude was upbeat and positive.

She is now 83 and cancer-free! She is the strongest person I know and an incredible example for all of our family and friends. Mother has always loved gardening, and says that it has been therapeutic and healing for her.

She has the gift of being a survivor, and creating beautiful flower gardens. My painting depicts her in a serene moment with a dahlia of rainbow colors. The halo represents her thoughts of flowers she has grown, and flowers she will grow in her future.

CONNECT

Relate what you see to your own life.
What does the work remind you of?
Why? How does it compare to other
images you have seen?

◀ A SECOND CHANCE
Watercolor by a Person Diagnosed with Cancer
Florida, United States

After my friend, Joy, had a double mastectomy, she had butterflies tattooed on the bare canvas of her chest. She wanted something lovely there where her breasts had been. She wanted something to represent her second chance after her terrible ordeal with breast cancer.

Each time I navigate through my journey with breast cancer, I wonder, will I get a second chance? Twenty-six years ago, as I was wheeled into surgery for a mastectomy, I wondered if I would see my children graduate high school. Two recurrences and two metastases later, I've seen my children graduate college, marry and have families. I've realized, like my friend's flurry of butterflies, that I'm having my second chance. Again, and again, and again, and again, and again.

---

left page
◀ GROWING
Watercolor by a Person Diagnosed with Cancer
Texas, United States

Being diagnosed with breast cancer was an unexpected and terrible blow, but after going through the chemo and radiation I gradually began to heal, which strengthened my desire to live. The power of faith in healing and gratitude to God for all the wonderful blessings He had given me as well as my husband, family and friends nourished my growth through this valley.

This painting shows the horrible crab of cancer as it invaded my left breast. The vivid, bright colors and the lively movement of my body depict a body that is healing and alive.

Our walk in life is made up of times when we are on the highest mountains and other times when we walk through the valleys. The valleys are where we grow.

◀ MOM'S TEARS
Watercolor by a Family Member, Friend, or Caregiver
Massachusetts, United States

When mom learned that she had breast cancer for the second time, she handled the news with faith, strength and grace. If she cried, I didn't see it. She suffered in silence, staying strong for her family. "Mom's Tears" is about her journey.

The misshapen heart represents the impact of cancer therapy on her body and soul. The teardrop at the tip renders the visible sorrow. Tears hidden throughout portray masked suffering. A shaft of light represents guiding faith. The hidden tear here shows God sharing her grief. Rainbow colors render the personal attributes that sustained her: red for love and courage, orange for cheerfulness, yellow for optimism, green for durability, blue for honor and peace, purple for elegance, and brown for endurance.

▲

TRANSITION
Mixed Media by a Family Member, Friend, or Caregiver
California, United States

I was with my mother when she received the phone call from her doctor telling her she had breast cancer. It was as though a shadow was descending on me, encroaching on the safety and security of my life. The darkness continued to obscure my perception until I was physically and emotionally distant, across the country at school for my final semester. When I adjusted to the isolation from my mother and her treatment, the unrest transformed into the realization that this journey was about light emerging from darkness: my mother conquering cancer and teaching me about life through her strength and positivity.

This piece depicts how my mother's cancer diagnosis affected me, by abstractly defining three words that encompass my perception of this experience.

IT'S A WONDERFUL WORLD
Oil by a Family Member, Friend, or Caregiver
Alabama, United States

I am a five-year breast cancer survivor. I stopped painting, which was my favorite hobby, for several years because of hand tremors. During my bout with cancer, I started painting again. I often have to use two hands to hold the brush. This painting of my daughter reflects a labor of love. It is a wonderful world because she is still in it. About a year ago, she was diagnosed with breast cancer. Surgery, chemo and radiation followed. About a week after beginning chemo, she lost her hair. Isn't she beautiful? She now has hair and is cancer free. It is definitely a wonderful world.

HEALING WALK
Photography by a Person Diagnosed with Cancer
Indiana, United States

After my breast cancer diagnosis, the walks my husband and I took at a nearby state park had a new meaning. Each hike in the woods felt like a healing journey, the fresh air and the beauty of nature surrounding us. It gave me a sense of peace and calm during a frightening time.

And now, after my treatments are done, seeing the beauty in all the different seasons keeps me in balance and brings happiness to my soul.

▲

DANCING ACROSS THE BIG "C"
Watercolor by a Person Diagnosed with Cancer
Minnesota, United States

It was cancer—breast cancer. My mind numb from information, my emotions spent from worry. Lumpectomy, radiation and pills for five years. So I started dancing.

It was cancer—skin cancer. What glorious years in the sun, dashed with reality of too much, too much. Chunks of skin removed with care, as I kept on dancing.

It was cancer—breast cancer. Ten years in between, surprise, surprise. No question now, the breast has to go. Greatly supported by family and friends, so I'll keep on dancing.

It is health; it is hope. It is sky and earth, water and rock. It is life still full of adventures, and playing and laughing, and I am dancing, dancing forever.

▲

VOICES OF WOMEN BUTTERFLY QUILT
Photography by a Person Diagnosed with Cancer
Minnesota, United States

The "Voices of Women Butterfly Quilt" celebrates my 5th anniversary as a breast cancer survivor, and is a metaphor for the transformative experience of breast reconstruction after mastectomy. The butterfly hovers in an abstract forest clearing—trees and dark foliage behind, flowers blooming in the transition to sunlight at woods edge. Is she basking in sunshine or emitting her own glow? The border represents a circle of accomplished women, singing a message of support for all who have or will be battling breast cancer. As I hand-sewed the quilt top, I thought of the meticulous stitches of my reconstructive surgeons, helping to put so many women back together after cancer, assisting their passage from darkness into light and into flight!

DIFFERENT, BUT STILL BEAUTIFUL
Photography by a Person Diagnosed with Cancer
New Hampshire, United States

Before I learned that I had DCIS, my definition of beauty was rather narrow. I sought out only the most unblemished and symmetrical blossoms to photograph, and failed to recognize how absolutely exquisite the imperfect can also be. However, my cancer diagnosis required me to make several important and irreversible decisions, including surgery. The results of my lumpectomy forced me to learn how to find value and beauty in a breast whose new appearance I once would've found to be shameful and ugly. My artwork evolved in response to this challenge. For example, I found this flower mesmerizing despite its scar. I feel blessed that my ongoing cancer journey has taught me to appreciate that which is different, but still beautiful.

TRANSFORMED
Mixed Media by a Person Diagnosed with Cancer
Minnesota, United States

Hearing the words, "You have breast cancer," was paralyzing! My fear was replaced by an amazing medical team, hope through prayer and support from family and friends. Focusing on the positive challenged me to resume watercolor again. I learned to express my feelings in a non-representational way, enjoying the spontaneity of letting colors mix and textures happen. As a result, I opened the door to a new way of seeing the world!

The blue threads signify cancer and the yellow cross signifies faith. I used my flower photos, but modified them to represent me after cancer. The new flowers are as beautiful as the original photos, like me before cancer and now as a survivor, celebrating the gift of life with joy and inner peace!

DESCRIBE

Try using expressive language when
describing all the things you see.
Instead of saying, "I see the sky," you
might say, "I see a dark, foreboding sky
full of heavy clouds."

I AM ALIVE
see artwork narrative on page 29

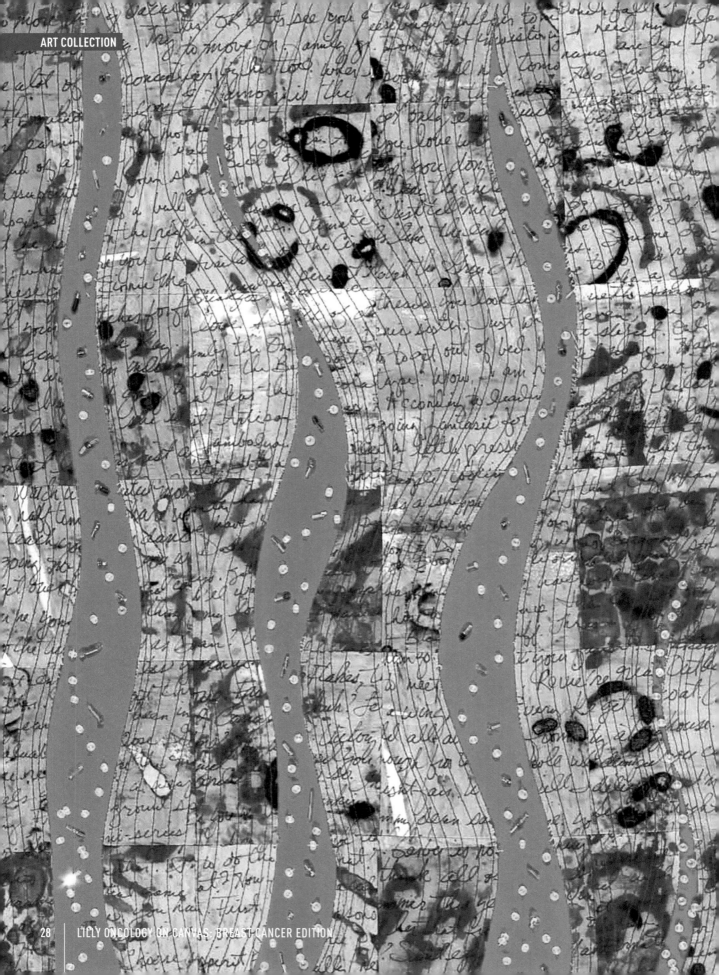

◀ **I AM ALIVE**
Acrylic by a Person Diagnosed with Cancer
Indiana, United States

I am twice a survivor: First of breast cancer and a few years later of urinary bladder cancer, not related to each other.

After the diagnosis of cancer, both times, I went through several emotional steps: surprise, confusion, despair, expectation, hope, and recovery.

Today I am alive.

In my painting I am looking with joy at the dawn of a new day and a bright future. LIVE while you are alive.

left page
◀ **CHEMO**
Mixed Media by a Person Diagnosed with Cancer
Utah, United States

I was diagnosed with breast cancer in January 2012, and I'm currently halfway through chemotherapy. As a long-time quilter, I've expressed my journey through my fabric work. I hand-dye all my fabrics, starting with 100 percent white cotton.

This quilt shows the work of chemo as it flows through the port into my blood stream. The colored beads represent the chemo, and the white beads signify white blood cells helping my body move towards health. I visualize the future in the smallest plume on the left side of the quilt, a time when my blood stream will carry plenty of white blood cells—no chemo or cancer present.

I designed and made this quilt, using a combination of machine and hand stitching.

◀ **THE CRUCIBLE**
Photography by a Person Diagnosed with Cancer
Arkansas, United States

The dictionary defines a crucible as a test of faith, patience or strength. For me, cancer became the crucible in which my faith, patience and strength were tested. Five years after a diagnosis of tongue cancer and two years since a diagnosis of breast cancer, I am alive and well and stronger than ever, especially mentally and spiritually. It may sound strange, but cancer was a gift that changed my life and made me a better person.

▲

HELP ALONG THE WAY
Mixed Media by a Person Diagnosed with Cancer
Arkansas, United States

Cancer is a journey you do not want to make alone. If you are fortunate, it is pieced together by a support system of family, friends, church, prayers, doctors, medicine, and strangers. The rough road through cancer is then diminished by their help along the way, which is similar to the journey of slaves escaping bondage of slavery to freedom—quilts holding hidden codes used to guide them through.

The shoofly quilt pattern used along the Underground Railroad identified a place or person who knew the codes and could provide food, shelter or guidance. This shoofly quilt represents my journey escaping the bondage of breast cancer to freedom. This piece is dedicated to those who helped along the way. Love was the string tied with hope.

GODDESS OF STRENGTH

Mixed Media by a Person Diagnosed with Cancer
Florida, United States

Fear of the unknown.

A lump not shown.

Tests bring the diagnosis not wanting to hear.

Breast Cancer becomes the message that I fear.

Loss of hair, sickness, weakness through the chemo was to be.

The daily routine was needed for a positive outcome to date for me.

Over 4 years have passed from the beginning of my strife.

Good health, family and friends are the most important things in life.

If not for the doctors, nurses, and all the other medical groups for their access.
The treatments for cancer would never be in progress.

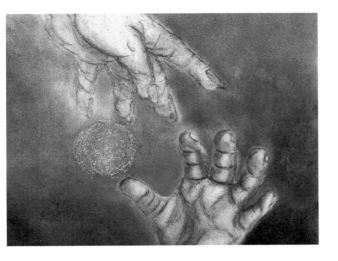

TOUCH LIFE
Mixed Media by a Person Diagnosed with Cancer
Alabama, United States

There are four girls in my family and it seems that all of us inherited the dreaded generational bad genes. All four of us have survived breast cancer, but now suffer from a list of chronic conditions, as well as other cancers. I used to be an educator and now I use my hands to create, to give and to mentor.

I do all I can to maintain my quality of life. Keeping my doctor's appointments, enduring biopsies, needle pricks, probes, nausea, chills, and the long waits among strangers who share the common bond. Each day is a surprise filled with anticipation. At the sounds of the morning birds as they lift their chirping towards the sunrise, I know it's a fresh new day. I reach out and touch the gift of life. I breathe, I unfold and once again my faith grows stronger.

left page
BLOSSOMING
Mixed Media by a Person Diagnosed with Cancer
Washington, United States

Being diagnosed with breast cancer has been a life changing experience. Joining a cancer art therapy group has helped me understand, cope with and even grow from it.

My artwork consists of pieces from watercolors I've done in my group. The colors represent the emotions I've felt: fear, anger, sadness—but also joy and triumph.

The butterflies depict group members who have surrounded me with love and support. I am blessed to have their help on my journey, and honored to be part of theirs. They are my role models, my heroes.

The flower symbolizes how cancer and art therapy have changed my life. They have made me pay attention to what is important. I am the flower. I have grown. I have blossomed...

THE PERENNIAL LEMONADE TREE
Mixed Media by a Person Diagnosed with Cancer
Kentucky, United States

I have enjoyed being an amateur gardener and using the creative part of my brain. During chemo, many days were spent lethargic and weary. However, my mind wandered into creative thoughts and ideas like never before. I didn't have the strength to garden that summer, but I could sit out back in my tree house deck and create in my daydreams.

My cancer journey was like that of a perennial plant. Bilateral mastectomy, reconstruction, and chemo break one down to the core—loss of breasts, hair, all things we think of as womanly. But, like a perennial, each season brings new growth and experiences. I learned to make lemonade from my lemons.

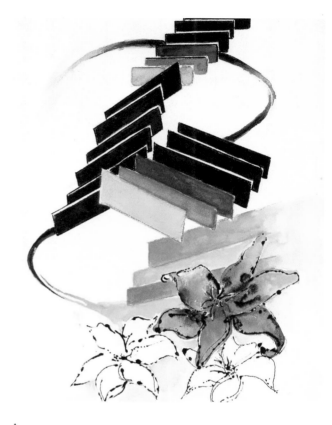

I AM BEAUTIFUL TO HIM

Watercolor by a Person Diagnosed with Cancer
Texas, United States

This is my husband.

He loves me no matter what, no eyebrows, no hair, no breasts.
I am beautiful to him.

He is my caregiver and friend, my chef and chauffeur. He lightens
my load and makes me laugh.

He lets others who love me know what's going on, always with
a positive tone and a reminder to keep praying.

He is my prayer warrior, always reminding me to choose faith over fear.

We trust God's grace, His plans, timing and His power to do
the impossible.

Cancer has brought me many blessings, including showing
me what a wonderful man my husband is.

I can't imagine this journey without him.

CANCER JOURNEY STEPS

Mixed Media by a Person Diagnosed with Cancer
Arizona, United States

1998: "So—you have
breast cancer."

Step-by-step:
doctor visits, tests, surgery,
radiation, medicines...
I felt my body betrayed me.

Weeks, months, years—
then the news.

2006: "So—your cancer
has recurred."

Step-by-step:
all the "hormones" failed,
tumor-marker numbers
went up, lots of pain,
other medical problems
appeared…

I felt so angry.

2010: "So—you need to
try something different."

This time:
chemo, lab work, oncology
visits, injections...
I felt my body was
my enemy.

Weeks, months, years and
then, finally, good news.

2012: "So—hope you feel
as good as your PET scan
pictures look!"

The red flower represents
no evidence of disease.
The other flowers—
my unknown future.

THE ART OF VIEWING ART

LOOK

Look at the art for 30 seconds, and
then look away. Try to remember
everything you saw, and look
again. What did you remember?
What did you overlook?

A WILD JOURNEY
see artwork narrative on page 37

A WILD JOURNEY
Mixed Media by a Person Diagnosed with Cancer
North Carolina, United States

A road map of life,
A collage filled with lots
Of support and love.
A life of goals,
Freedom to create and achieve,
Inspired from above.
A happy journey from
Australia to the USA.
A very successful teaching.

Career so they say,
A surprise wild cancer journey
Of twist and turns,
breast and bone,
A joining of lost family coming
Home.
Feeling the love,
Never alone!

---

left page
BACKSTORY
Photography by a Person Diagnosed with Cancer
Texas, United States

Friends look at me, a breast cancer survivor, and say that I sailed through treatment with grace and style. Maybe that's what they saw, but I want them to know that days felt like months and weeks, like years. There were endless diagnostic tests, countless doctor's appointments, surgeries, needles, blood draws, waiting, pain, worrying, praying, pleading, and tears.

I want them to know that I felt insanely jealous when I saw someone's hair blowing in the wind, and I longed to feel what that was like again.

If I had to do it all over again, I'd be more honest, accept more visits and embrace my family and friends' affirming love even tighter.

BEAUTIFULLY BALD
Photography by a Family Member, Friend, or Caregiver
Washington, United States

It doesn't seem possible that two-and-a-half years have passed since the initial diagnosis of breast cancer. My daughter-in-law, Jen, was just too young.

Jen was told that she would most definitely lose her beautiful, long, blonde locks. That lovely hair that she always stroked so lovingly as it hung by the side of her face. Losing her breasts wasn't nearly as difficult as knowing she would lose her hair. So she and two of her friends all shaved their heads. I'm sure that it was a shock to her at first but, after that initial shock, her inner beauty shone right on through.

She was beautiful. She is beautiful. She has gone through hair loss three times—always smiling, always loving, always hoping for a cure.

▲

NOT INVISIBLE, NOT ALONE
Acrylic by a Family Member, Friend, or Caregiver
Arkansas, United States

My mother's journey with cancer started in 1994, with a mastectomy. Then, later, invasive lung surgery. Chemo—with both. In the last 3 years she's had lung cancer again. They used a new method of freezing it, and it went fine. Then she had cancer on her nose, which was removed. Now she has breast cancer in lymph nodes in her neck. She knows she's not strong enough for chemo—so she's taking injections once a month. Then a PET scan every 3, to see if it's working. So far everything's good. We have an appointment with the doctor tomorrow. Hopefully still fine.

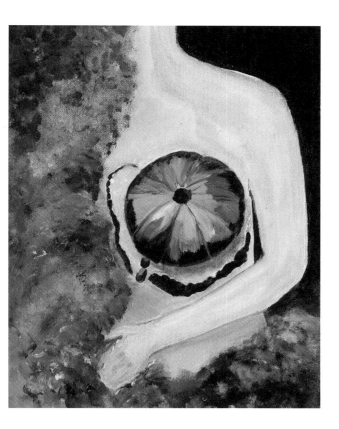

A LUMP AS BIG AS AN ORANGE
Oil by a Person Diagnosed with Cancer
Florida, United States

When I was diagnosed with breast cancer, the words "you have a lump as big as an orange" stunned me. How could I have had no pain—not even a heavy feeling? "Mammograms can't see this type of cancer." Impossible. I'd had a mammogram every year for 20 years. I couldn't wait to get this monster out of me.

The journey began. It consumed my life: tests, double mastectomy, lymph node surgery, physical therapy to regain use of my arms, breast reconstruction, healing touch, wonderful care, support from so many people, unexpected acts of kindness, positive thinking. Two years later, no cancer cells but still healing emotionally. I am so grateful. I'm so glad to be alive. Thank you, God.

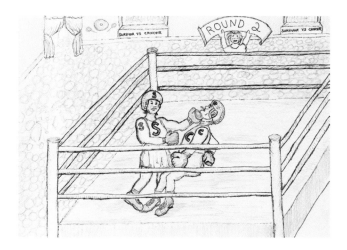

CANCER WANTS A RE-MATCH
Mixed Media by a Person Diagnosed with Cancer
Massachusetts, United States

The gloves were hung up for 25 years and then they came out of retirement for round two.

Breast cancer had snuck up on me in late summer when I was 33-years old. It was a quick fight, biopsy, lumpectomy, surgery, tattoos, radiation, and a couple of months later, radiation seeds.

Twenty-five long years had gone by until my arm started to swell and I woke up in bad pain. A CAT scan and ultrasound showed a mass around my subclavical vein.

Round two is about to begin. Breast cancer had found its way under my collarbone. Now I've had three biopsies, surgery and radiation under my belt. I am waiting for the knockout punch when I have my next PET scan.

DING DING DING! And the winner is…?

◄ **WORLDS AWAY**
Pastel by a Person Diagnosed with Cancer
Ohio, United States

Living every day as though it was the most important day of your life is the strongest defiance that one has against the devastation of cancer. One may not always come out on top of the disease, but is always able to be victorious if each day of one's life brings new wonders, joys and triumphs. Being diagnosed more than three decades ago with breast cancer is the heaviest burden I have faced. But the diagnosis has had a defining influence on my life and many others' lives. The lone individual is able to take in the beauty of nature and the human homage to wonder. I have found that the world and the gestures of humanity never disappoint whenever people allow themselves to be in awe.

left page
◄ **LOVE BLOOMS**
Mixed Media by a Person Diagnosed with Cancer
Pennsylvania, United States

My cancer journey began when I was diagnosed with breast cancer at age 44. I received a few phone calls from close family and friends, but most just didn't know what to say. What can you say when it's cancer? Then the cards began to arrive—from friends and family near and far, co-workers, acquaintances, and some from people I didn't even know. "Get Well" and "Thinking of You" cards, funny cards and inspirational cards—all filled with words of love, support and prayers.

Too pretty to throw out and full of so much heartfelt love, I have saved all those cards. This artwork was created using little pieces of those words, wishes and sentiments all embedded in a beautiful bouquet that will forever bloom.

◄ **CROSSING HIGH WATERS**
Watercolor by a Person Diagnosed with Cancer
Wisconsin, United States

When I was diagnosed with breast cancer, I was absolutely terrified. I felt there would never be security or happiness again in my life. But, I survived and thrived. The best years of my life have been since cancer, because it reminded me of my mortality. It nudged me to make the best of my time, which I've succeeded at.

My watercolor painting depicts cancer as treacherous, jagged rocks and churning, cold water below. Once crossed, the rocks give way to tranquil shores to sure footing and, once again, life is secure, comfortable, colorful, and deeply appreciated and cherished.

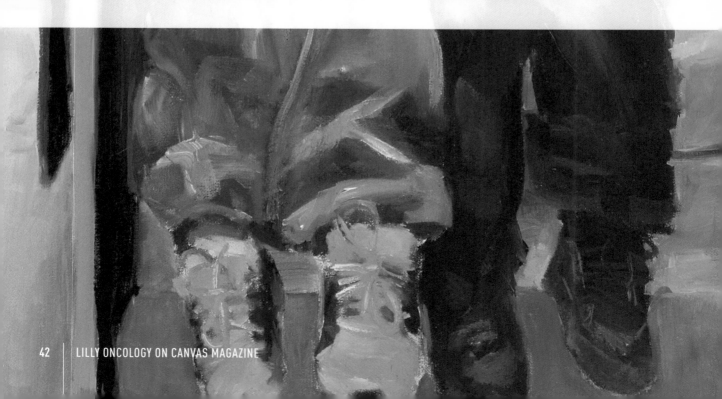

LOOC ART
ON TOUR

FINDING STRENGTH THROUGH ART

"Your cancer has spread." The words no one wants to hear. But in those four words, many find a depth of courage they never dreamed possible. A determination to find beauty in every moment, and to never give in. This inward transformation becomes evident in the outward expression of shape, color, texture, words—and ultimately, hope.

◄ **STRONG AND FREE IN SPIRIT**
Photography by a Family Member, Friend, or Caregiver
Maryland, United States

The inspiration for this photograph stems from the role of Evey Hammond, played by Natalie Portman, in the movie "V for Vendetta." A specific portion of the movie depicts her being tortured, beaten and trampled on for information, which she refuses to disclose. When she is sentenced to be executed, she remains at peace with her choice and steadfast in her beliefs.

My wife, through her focus, embodies these qualities. Amidst her diagnosis of metastatic breast cancer that has metastasized to her liver and bones, the 6 rounds of chemotherapy, her bilateral mastectomy, the 6+ weeks of radiation, the hormone therapy, and her upcoming bilateral oophorectomy, she remains an adoring wife, an incredible mother to our twin toddler boys and the embodiment of courage.

"...She remains an adoring wife, an incredible mother to our twin toddler boys and the embodiment of courage."

"As each flower has its own place and time to bloom, so each of us has our own road in the Journey through the Fog."

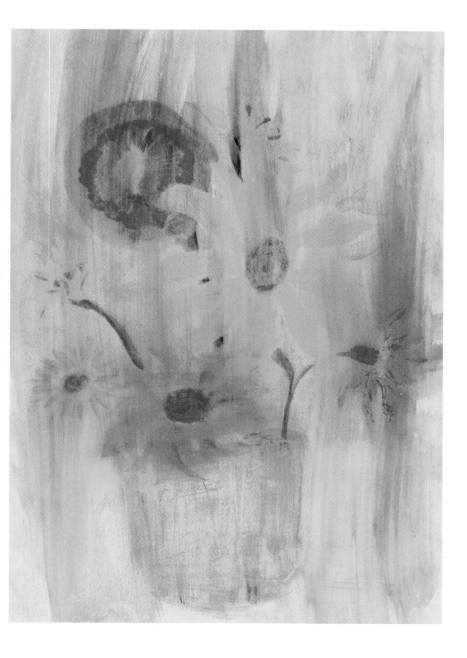

◄ **FLOWERS THROUGH THE FOG**
Watercolor by a Person Diagnosed with Cancer
Arkansas, United States

I was diagnosed with breast cancer in 2001. In 2011, it came back in my lung and bones, and after more chemo I am learning to live with cancer.

My Journey is reflected in my painting. Whether you're a bud or a flower in full bloom, going through the fog of cancer treatment is part of the Journey. As each flower has its own place and time to bloom, so each of us has our own road in the Journey through the Fog.

Because of the Fog, I see the World in the Light. I am thankful for all the people who have helped me in this Journey, whether they helped with my medical treatment, were my support group, or were the person who smiled at my bald head.

▲

THE SPIRIT OF HONU
Photography by a Person Diagnosed with Cancer
Illinois, United States

This photo was taken on our last family vacation before my stage IV breast cancer diagnosis. At the time, I felt an urgent need to visit our family in Hawaii. I'm eternally grateful for this wonderful experience. My children met their extended family, and we had many spontaneous encounters with Hawaiian sea turtles. We saw these majestic creatures everywhere—it was as if they were watching over us. The turtle in my photograph approached us and I was in complete awe of this ancient soul. I pondered how she could be strong and powerful in the water, yet graceful and peaceful on land. Her peace surrounded me. Now, on my cancer journey, I call upon her gift of strength, perseverance and grace as I remember the Spirit of Honu.

"I pondered how she could be strong and powerful in the water, yet graceful and peaceful on land. Her peace surrounded me."

"I persevere with the knowledge that with all this support, my spirit will be eternally uplifted."

◀ **UPLIFTED**
Acrylic by a Person Diagnosed with Cancer
Tennessee, United States

During the past 6 years, stage IV breast cancer has brought loss and sorrow from the depths of darkness. I have received such an outpouring of love and compassion from friends and family giving me inspiration and encouragement. Their continued support for my every need is tremendous, making an almost unbearable situation turn into an experience of healing. It empowers me to face every day with an attitude of gratitude and to continue reaching for the stars. I wanted to create a permanent expression of my gratefulness and pay tribute to everyone, including my doctors, nurses, therapists, and counselors who continue to provide treatment and professional guidance. I persevere with the knowledge that with all this support, my spirit will be eternally uplifted.

◀ **LIFE NESTED**
Acrylic by a Person Diagnosed with Cancer
Colorado, United States

I am an artist and mother of two young children in my third year of survivorship with metastatic breast cancer. After a year of enduring a bilateral mastectomy, chemotherapy and cyber knife for metastases to my liver, I was awarded remission. Seven months later, my vision became blurred, and a met was found in my brain. After cyber knifing, I was awarded remission again. Five months later, another tumor was spotted in my brain and treated with whole brain radiation.

"Life Nested" represents moving from the questioning period of survivorship into acceptance and the need to live fully. The nest is empty and needs to be filled. There is a sense of joy and prayer. At the same time, the breasts bleed and mourn.

"'Life Nested' represents moving from the questioning period of survivorship into acceptance and the need to live fully."

"This includes friends, family and doctors shining a light in the mission to embrace adversity gracefully."

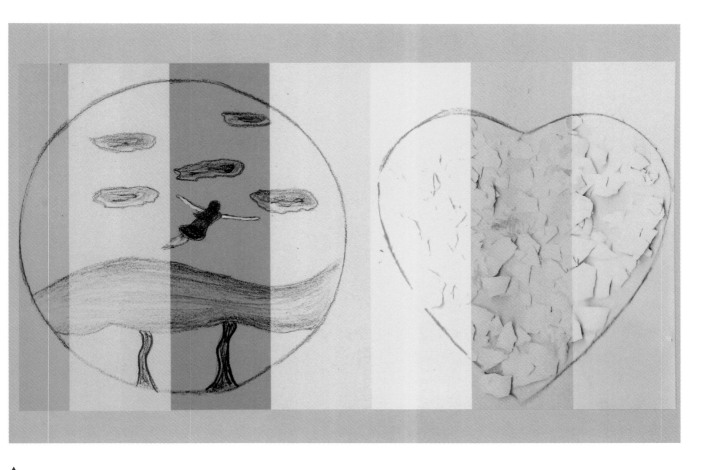

FLYING OVER EGGSHELLS
Mixed Media by a Family Member, Friend, or Caregiver
New York , United States

My mom was diagnosed with stage 4 hormone-receptor-positive breast cancer in August of 2011. Upon returning home from a tropical vacation with my dad, a lump was noticed on the side of her left eye. After a planned procedure to remove what was thought to be just a mass, more testing was done to determine the cancer diagnosis. My art shows the initial shock of life as she saw it, as we all saw it, crumpling into pieces. We were all literally "walking on eggshells," jumping to conclusions too hastily. And then slowly, pulling the pieces together with strength and a loving support system. This includes friends, family and doctors shining a light in the mission to embrace adversity gracefully.

▲

SEVEN RAYS OF HEALING
Mixed Media by a Person Diagnosed with Cancer
New Jersey, United States

I was diagnosed with stage IV metastasized breast cancer in 2009. Since then, I have been under the care of my oncologist. In addition to chemo and radiation, I have introduced into my life supplementary treatments like meditation, visualization, journaling, art, and walks in nature. I have made friends with many like-minded cancer survivors. Even though I am still receiving treatments, I consider myself a survivor. I am surviving every day. I wish to inspire and encourage other cancer survivors to embrace their journey with humor and courage.

"I wish to inspire and encourage other cancer survivors to embrace their journey with humor and courage."

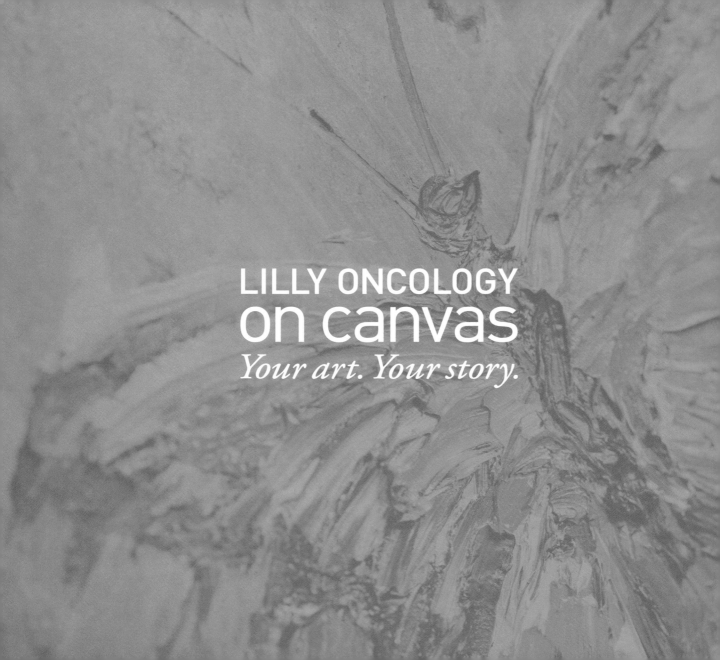

LILLY ONCOLOGY
on canvas
Your art. Your story.